This book belongs to . . .

....

OXFORD
UNIVERSITY PRESS

Great Clarendon Street, Oxford, OX2 6DP, United Kingdom

Oxford University Press is a department of the University of Oxford.
It furthers the University's objective of excellence in research, scholarship
and education by publishing worldwide. Oxford is a registered trade mark
of Oxford University Press in the UK and in certain other countries

British Library Cataloguing in Publication Data
Data available

ISBN: 978-0-19-273454-9

10 9 8 7 6 5 4 3 2 1

Typeset in OUP Earlybird

Printed in China

Paper used in the production of this book is a natural, recyclable product
made from wood grown in sustainable forests. The manufacturing process
conforms to the environmental regulations of the country of origin.

Acknowledgements

Series Advisor: Nikki Gamble

Help your child's learning
with essential tips, phonics
support and free eBooks
www.oxfordowl.co.uk

Oxford
Reading
Tree

Traditional Tales

The Tortoise and the Hare

and Other Stories

OXFORD
UNIVERSITY PRESS

Tips for reading Rabbit on the Run together

About the story

This story is a simple retelling of Aesop's fable 'The Tortoise and the Hare'.

This book practises these letter patterns:

s a t p i m d g o k e u r h b
f l ff w x qu ck sh ng

Ask your child to point to these letters or letter pairs and say the sounds.

Your child might find these words tricky:

was you me

Say these words for your child if they do not know them.

- Before you begin, ask your child to read the title to you by sounding out and blending. Talk about what the story might be about. Do you think Rabbit looks like a good runner?

- Encourage your child to read the story to you. Talk about the pictures as you read.

- Your child will be able to read most of the words in the story, but if they struggle with a word, remind them to say the sounds in the word from left to right. Ask them to point to the sounds as they say them, and then blend the sounds into a whole word, e.g. sh-o-t, shot.

- After you have read the story, look through it again and talk about why Rabbit was so sure he would win. What would he do differently next time?

- Do the fun activity together!

Rabbit on the Run

Written by Alex Lane

Illustrated by Laura Hughes

OXFORD
UNIVERSITY PRESS

Rabbit was quick.

9

Rabbit was on the run.

Hang on!

Rabbit shot off.

Rabbit ran and ran.

You cannot get me!

Rabbit had a nap.

Rabbit got up.

Rabbit was in a rush.

Run the Race

Can you retell the story of the race?

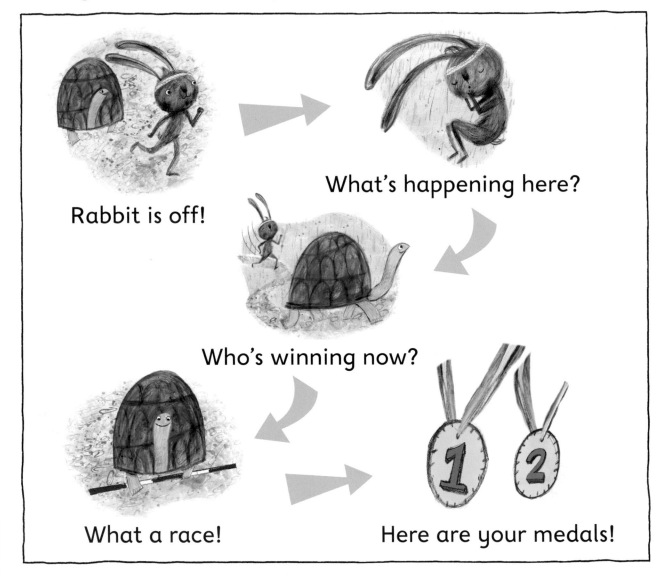

Rabbit is off!

What's happening here?

Who's winning now?

What a race!

Here are your medals!

You could pretend to be Rabbit and Tortoise and race too!

Tips for reading I Will Get You together

This story is a simple retelling of the Norwegian tale 'The Three Billy Goats Gruff'. In Norway trolls often appear in stories as strong, unkind creatures.

This book practises these letter patterns:

s a t p i n m d g o c k e u r
h b f l w x ck ll ff th ng qu

Ask your child to point to these letters or letter pairs and say the sounds.

Your child might find these words tricky:

he   me   you

Say these words for your child if they do not know them.

- Before you begin, ask your child to read the title to you by sounding out and blending. Talk about what the story might be about. Look through the story to find the three goats and the troll.

- Encourage your child to read the story to you. Talk about the pictures as you read.

- Your child will be able to read most of the words in story, but if they struggle with a word, remind them to say the sounds in the word from left to right. Ask them to point to the sounds as they say them, and then blend the sounds into a whole word, e.g. qu-a-ck, quack.

- After you have read the story, look through it again and talk about what happened. Who do you think was the strongest character in the story?

- Do the fun activity together!

I Will Get You

Written by Alex Lane

Illustrated by Elle Daly

OXFORD
UNIVERSITY PRESS

Tip, tap, tip, tap ...

Tip, tap, tip, tap

Off he ran.

Yum-yum!
Yes, I will get him.

Tip, tap, tip, tap ...
... along the path.

Tip,
tap,
tip,
tap

Quack!

Off he ran.

Yum-yum!
Yes, I will get him.

Off he ran!

Bang!

Quack, quack, quack!

Make the sounds!

Let's make the sounds each billy goat makes as he crosses the bridge.

Tip, tap, tip, tap

Which billy goat is the quietest?
Which billy goat is the loudest?

What noise do you think the troll is making now?

Tips for reading The King and His Wish together

About the story

This story is a simple retelling of the Carribean tale from the Dominican Republic called 'The King who wanted to touch the moon'.

This book practises these letter patterns:

s a t p i m d g o k e u r h b
f l w x ll ng th sh

Ask your child to point to these letters or letter pairs and say the sounds.

Your child might find these words tricky:

he   me   you   all

Say these words for your child if they do not know them.

- Before you begin, ask your child to read the title to you by sounding out and blending. Talk about what the story might be about. How can you tell this man is a king? What do you think he will wish for?

- Encourage your child to read the story to you. Talk about the pictures as you read.

- Your child will be able to read most of the words in the story, but if they struggle with a word, remind them to say the sounds in the word from left to right. Ask them to point to the sounds as they say them, and then blend the sounds into a whole word, e.g. w-i-sh, wish.

- After you have read the story, look through it again and talk about what happened. What do you think the King learned that day?

- Do the fun activity together!

The King and His Wish

Written by Alison Hawes

Illustrated by Kate Slater

OXFORD
UNIVERSITY PRESS

The King had a wish.

44

45

The King got a big, red box.

49

51

54

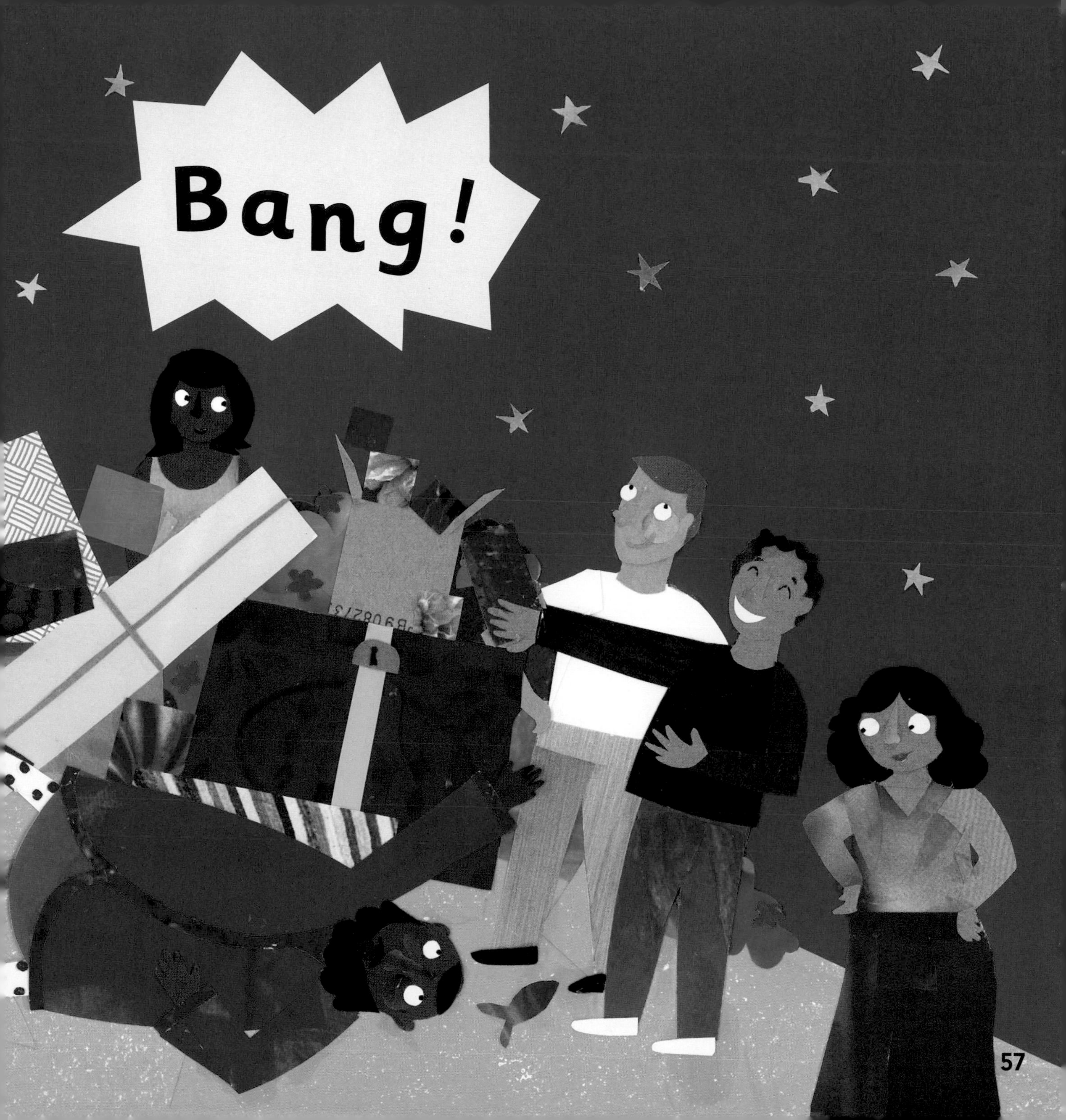
Bang!

How many?

The king tried to get up very, very high!

How many boxes and parcels can you count in the tower?

Which one is your favourite?

What do you think would be inside it?

Tips for reading Dick and His Cat together

About the story

This story is a simple retelling of the British folk tale known as 'Dick Whittington and His Cat'. It is a favourite story for Christmas pantomimes.

This book practises these letter patterns:

s a t p i m d g o k e u r h b
f l s w x ck ss ll ch ng sh

Ask your child to point to these letters or letter pairs and say the sounds.

Your child might find these words tricky:

be was Say these words for your child if they do not know them.

- Before you begin, ask your child to read the title to you by sounding out and blending. Talk about what the story might be about. What are cats good at? Turn to page 68 for the answer.

- Encourage your child to read the story to you. Talk about the pictures as you read.

- Your child will be able to read most of the words in the story, but if they struggle with a word, remind them to say the sounds in the word from left to right. Ask them to point to the sounds as they say them, and then blend the sounds into a whole word, e.g. c-a-sh, cash.

- After you have read the story, look through it again and talk about what happened. Why did Dick get so much money? What do you think he did next?

- Do the fun activity together!

Dick
and
His Cat

Written by Katie Adams

Illustrated by Sue Mason

OXFORD
UNIVERSITY PRESS

Dick got his bag.

63

Dick met a man.

The man got Dick a job.

Dick got a cat.

Dick got a bag of cash.

Dick got lots of jobs.

The cat got lots of rats.

Hiss! Hiss!

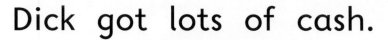

Dick got lots of cash.

Dick was rich!

I am rich! Rich! Rich!

Find the rhyme

Find the three things that rhyme.

Practise Your Phonics With
★ Traditional Tales ★

More stories for you to enjoy...

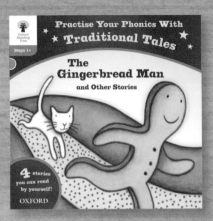
Practise Your Phonics With
Traditional Tales
Stage 1+
The Gingerbread Man
and Other Stories
4 stories you can read by yourself!
OXFORD

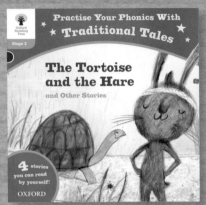
Practise Your Phonics With
Traditional Tales
Stage 2
The Tortoise and the Hare
and Other Stories
4 stories you can read by yourself!
OXFORD

Coming soon...

Practise Your Phonics With
Traditional Tales
Stage 3
Chicken Licken
and Other Stories
4 stories you can read by yourself!
OXFORD

Practise Your Phonics With
Traditional Tales
Stage 4
The Man, the Boy and the Donkey
and Other Stories
4 stories you can read by yourself!
OXFORD

Practise Your Phonics With
Traditional Tales
Stage 5
Jack and the Beanstalk
and Other Stories
4 stories you can read by yourself!
OXFORD

Practise Your Phonics With
Traditional Tales
Stage 6
How the Bear Lost His Tail
and Other Stories
4 stories you can read by yourself!
OXFORD

Help your child's learning with essential tips, phonics support and free eBooks

www.oxfordowl.co.uk